THUNDERBIRDS™

TOP SECRET ANNUAL
2001

Sam Denham

CARLTON
BOOKS

THIS IS A CARLTON BOOK

Published by Carlton Books Limited 2000
20 Mortimer Street
London
W1N 7RD

Text and design © 2000 Carlton Books Limited

™ and © 1965 and 1999. THUNDERBIRDS is a trademark of Carlton International Media Limited
and is used under licence.
THUNDERBIRDS is a Gerry Anderson Production.
Licensed by Carlton International Media Limited.
© 1999. The CARLTON logotype device is a trademark of Carlton International Media Limited.

A CIP catalogue for this book is available from the British Library.

ISBN 1 84222 094 2

Project Editor: Lesley Levene
Language Consultant: Betty Root, formerly director of Reading Centre, University of Reading
Design: Carol Wright
Production: Garry Lewis

To: All International Rescue Agents

From: Jeff Tracy

Security File Code: Top Secret Annual 2001

Message Starts: Hi there...

As one of International Rescue's worldwide network of agents, you've been given special clearance to receive this top-secret videfile.

It contains all the essential facts you need to know about the International Rescue team, our fantastic Thunderbirds machines and our secret island base.

Brains and the team have also set you some special challenges to test your agent skills, and I've personally approved the release of an exciting mission report.

As this report shows, the security of International Rescue is a top priority, so take special care of this videfile to ensure that it does not fall into enemy hands.

Keep this frequency clear...F.A.B. ...Jeff Tracy.   **MESSAGE ENDS**

FILE CONTENTS

MISSION FILE REPORT: SECURITY HAZARD/VIDEPRINT ONE

Report Filed by: Jeff Tracy

"In the wrong hands, International Rescue's secrets could threaten the safety of the world, so the Thunderbirds craft are closely guarded while on call. But this time it looked like we'd met a hazard even we couldn't handle..."

IT ALL STARTED ON A RESCUE MISSION IN ENGLAND.

NO ONE COULD BE SPARED TO GUARD THUNDERBIRDS 1 AND 2...

...AND THEIR ARRIVAL HAD SEEMED LIKE A DREAM COME TRUE FOR YOUNG CHIP MORRISON, WHO WAS WATCHING THE OPERATION.

WOW! THUNDERBIRDS! I'D LOVE TO BE IN INTERNATIONAL RESCUE!

THE RESCUE OVER, THE BOYS RETURNED TO BASE - BUT VIRGIL HAD SERIOUS NEWS.

BETTER GET BRAINS TO STAND BY, FATHER. THERE'S A FAULT IN THUNDERBIRD 2.

LET'S GET IT FIXED AT ONCE, BRAINS. WE CAN'T AFFORD TO BE UNOPERATIONAL.

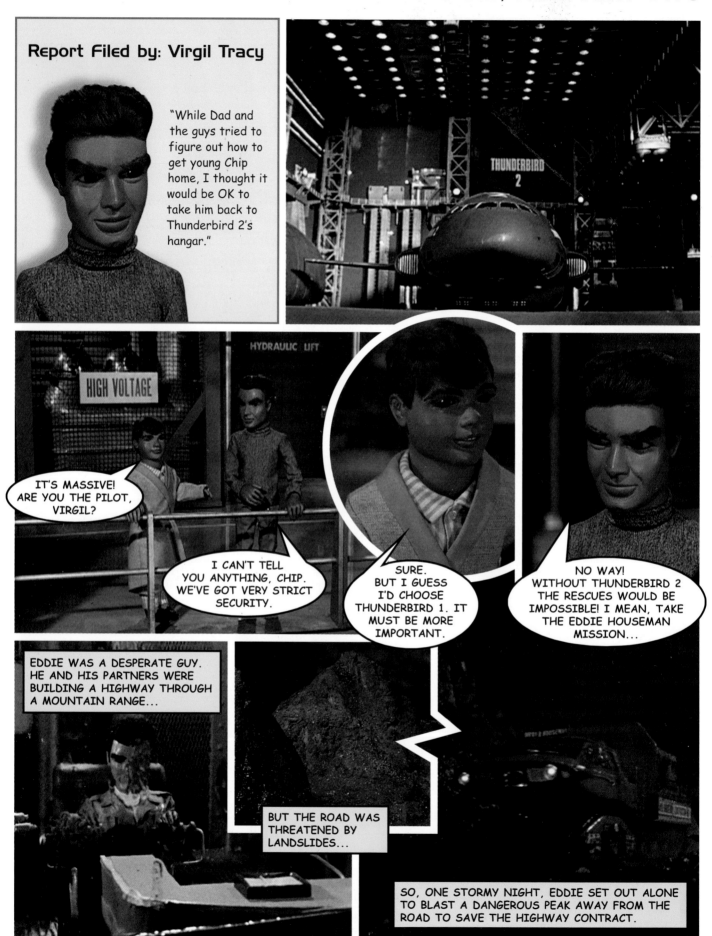

Report Filed by: Virgil Tracy

"While Dad and the guys tried to figure out how to get young Chip home, I thought it would be OK to take him back to Thunderbird 2's hangar."

THUNDERBIRD 2

HIGH VOLTAGE

HYDRAULIC LIFT

IT'S MASSIVE! ARE YOU THE PILOT, VIRGIL?

I CAN'T TELL YOU ANYTHING, CHIP. WE'VE GOT VERY STRICT SECURITY.

SURE. BUT I GUESS I'D CHOOSE THUNDERBIRD 1. IT MUST BE MORE IMPORTANT.

NO WAY! WITHOUT THUNDERBIRD 2 THE RESCUES WOULD BE IMPOSSIBLE! I MEAN, TAKE THE EDDIE HOUSEMAN MISSION...

EDDIE WAS A DESPERATE GUY. HE AND HIS PARTNERS WERE BUILDING A HIGHWAY THROUGH A MOUNTAIN RANGE...

BUT THE ROAD WAS THREATENED BY LANDSLIDES...

SO, ONE STORMY NIGHT, EDDIE SET OUT ALONE TO BLAST A DANGEROUS PEAK AWAY FROM THE ROAD TO SAVE THE HIGHWAY CONTRACT.

11

12

13

This is International Rescue

File issued by: Jeff Tracy

Top Secret...

Subject: International Rescue
Our equipment is way ahead of its time. In the wrong hands it could be used to destroy life. For this reason the information must be released only to authorized International Rescue agents.

Subject: Tracy Island

A beautiful island in the Pacific. Secret base of International Rescue. So far undetected. Outwardly the luxury home of millionaire ex-astronaut Jeff Tracy. But beneath its idyllic surface a maze of secret tunnels and hangars provide launch and maintenance facilities for International Rescue's fantastic fleet of vehicles.

Control Room: Tracy lounge
Launch areas:
Tracy Villa – Thunderbird 1
Cliff House – Thunderbirds 2 and 4
Round House – Thunderbird 3

Subject: Thunderbird 5

Reception Range: 100 million miles

Space Monitor – Capable of receiving or intercepting distress calls from any part of the world, Thunderbird 5 maintains a secret geo-stationary orbit high above the Earth. In addition to standard reception scanners, ultra-sensitive monitors equipped with global distress signal recognition filters guarantee immmediate response to emergency situations. Specialized equipment includes plasma-cored meteor deflector, electromagnetic anti-radar baffles and Star-fix geo-stationary orbit maintenance system.

Subject: Thunderbird 4

Maximum Speed: Classified

Capable of withstanding the pressures of the deeps, Thunderbird 4 is a versatile high-speed mini-sub. At 30 feet, it is the smallest of the Thunderbird craft. Its compact size means it can be flown to any rescue zone by Thunderbird 2, and can reach otherwise inaccessible underwater rescue sites. Powered by mini-atomic turbo drives, its specialized equipment includes laser cutting gear, hydraulic rams, undersea demolition missiles and hoverjets for emergency runway launch.

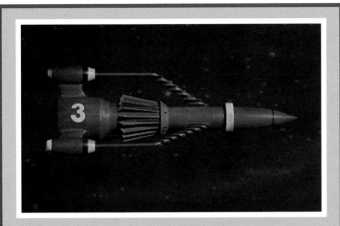

Subject: Thunderbird 3

Escape Velocity: 25,200 m.p.h.

Designed for space rescue and to provide a shuttle service to Thunderbird 5, its chemical rocket and atomic particle acceleration rocket propulsion technology enables Thunderbird 3 to travel immense distances through space. Although the craft can be flown by one man, a two-man crew is usually assigned for rescue missions. The specialized equipment carried on board includes a safety beam generator, space location scanners and astro rescue suits.

Subject: Thunderbird 2

Maximum Speed: 2,000 m.p.h.

A giant transporter, Thunderbird 2 carries all the rescue gear to the danger zone. It is the mainstay of the Thunderbird fleet, using an interchangeable pod system to load essential rescue equipment at short notice. At 250 feet long, 60 feet high and with a wing span of 180 feet, Thunderbird 2 is surprisingly manoeuvrable for its size. This is thanks to a combination of VTOL rockets, tail-mounted turbo-jets and twin side-mounted ram-jets. Specialized equipment includes forward-mounted grabs, magnetic clamps and a winch-mounted escape capsule.

Subject: Thunderbird 1

Maximum Speed : 15,000+ m.p.h.

Sleek, first and fast, Thunderbird 1's streamlined fuselage and central high-performance sustainer rocket enable it to reach phenomenal speeds, ensuring that it arrives at the rescue zone as quickly as possible to allow maximum time for detailed reconnaissance. With swing wings extended it is transformed into an aircraft with the aerodynamic flexibility of a fighter plane, while its vertical landing rockets ensure the touchdown precision of a helijet. Specialized equipment includes anti-camera devices, demolition cannon, sonar sounder and anti-avalanche spears.

Data File: The Tracy Family

Name: Jeff Tracy

Born: 2 January 2009

Special Duties: Mission Controller

Born on a Kansas wheat farm, an early interest in aerial crop maintenance and satellite-monitored harvesting technology led Jeff to join the US Air Force. His steely determination and flying skill impressed the International Space Agency, and he was recruited to its new lunar colonization programme. Jeff was one of the first men to return to the Moon, but tragedy struck with the death of his wife, and he gave up his space career to bring up his family and create Tracy Aerospace, a giant engineering company. His concern at the lack of coordinated disaster services following a serious aircrash led him to conceive a worldwide rapid response service – International Rescue.

Name: Scott Tracy

Born: 4 April 2039

Special Duties: Pilot Thunderbird 1

Named After: Astronaut Scott Carpenter

Educated at Oxford and Yale, Scott followed his father into the US Air Force. Decorated for bravery before leaving the service, he was the natural choice to pilot Thunderbird 1. His quick thinking, fierce determination and unfaltering bravery make him a natural leader, but his complete lack of arrogance means that his brothers can always rely on him to take on lesser tasks too. In Jeff's absence Scott usually takes any command decisions.

Name: Virgil Tracy

Born: 15 August 2041

Special Duties: Pilot Thunderbird 2

Named After: Astronaut Virgil Grissom

Inheriting his mother's artistic skills and his father's technical ability, Virgil graduated from the Denver School of Advanced Technology. Serious and thoughtful, he has a precise understanding of the capabilities of International Rescue's powerful technology, but is also aware of its limitations. As a result he is almost always required on rescue missions. Fearless and with an iron resolve, Virgil is probably the most practically minded of the Tracys.

Name: Alan Tracy

Born: 12 March 2044

Special Duties: Pilot Thunderbird 3

Named After: Astronaut Alan Shepherd

The youngest of the Tracy brothers, Alan's interest in space travel led him to embark on a range of ambitious rocket experiments while studying at Colorado University. Astronaut training followed, preparing him for the huge responsibility of piloting Thunderbird 3, but not before his love of motor-racing brought him fame as a champion driver. He is also an expert pot-holer and a great all-round sportsman. His romantic good looks make him a winner with the girls – particularly Tin-Tin.

Name: Gordon Tracy

Born: 14 February 2043

Special Duties: Pilot Thunderbird 4

Named After: Astronaut Gordon Cooper

Although his casual manner and often flippant attitude sometimes lead to conflict with his father, Gordon's rock-steady nerves and tenacious determination have gained him great respect as a member of International Rescue. His good-natured high spirits mask a deeper side – the result of his close shave with death in a high-speed hydrofoil crash. A keen water-skier and Olympic champion swimmer, Gordon's fascination with the sea led him to become an expert oceanographer and to develop a new design of aqualung, which has now been modified for rescue missions.

Name: John Tracy

Born: 8 October 2040

Special Duties: Space Monitor Thunderbird 5

Named After: Astronaut John Glenn

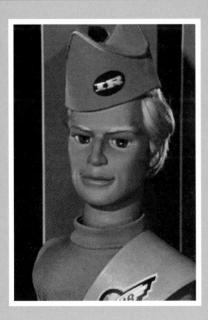

Educated at Harvard, John was the first of the Tracy boys to follow Jeff into space, becoming an astronaut and astro-communications expert. His skill and experience in this field naturally qualified him as duty commander of Thunderbird 5, although he alternates this responsibility with Alan. This gives him the chance to pursue his interest in astronomy. An expert in the field, his ceaseless quest to learn more about the universe has already resulted in the discovery of a new quasar system, named after his family, but his lack of direct experience with rescue missions is often a source of frustration.

Report Filed by: Alan Tracy

"When Virgil left me in charge of stowaway Chip Morrison, I guess I couldn't resist his request to see Thunderbird 3. After all, it is the Thunderbird fleet's most impressive ship."

SO THIS IS THE SPACE SHIP! HOW FAST DOES IT TRAVEL?

I CAN'T TELL YOU, CHIP - IT'S A SECRET.

BUT VIRGIL TOLD ME ALL ABOUT THUNDERBIRD 2.

WELL, HE SHOULDN'T HAVE.

I SUPPOSE BEING A SPACEMAN YOU DON'T GET SO INVOLVED WITH RESCUES.

NOT SO INVOLVED! I'M THE ONE THAT'S IN CHARGE WHEN THIS BABY BLASTS OFF INTO SPACE! YOU REMEMBER THE SUN PROBE ROCKET THAT WENT OUT OF CONTROL AND STARTED HEADING TOWARDS THE SUN?

AND INTERNATIONAL RESCUE HAD TO SAVE IT? SURE...

WELL, EVERYTHING WAS GOING ACCORDING TO PLAN. THE SOLARNAUTS' MISSION WAS TO COLLECT SAMPLES FROM THE OUTER REACHES OF THE SUN, AND THEY WERE PREPARING TO GO INTO ORBIT BEFORE FIRING THE PROBE -

21

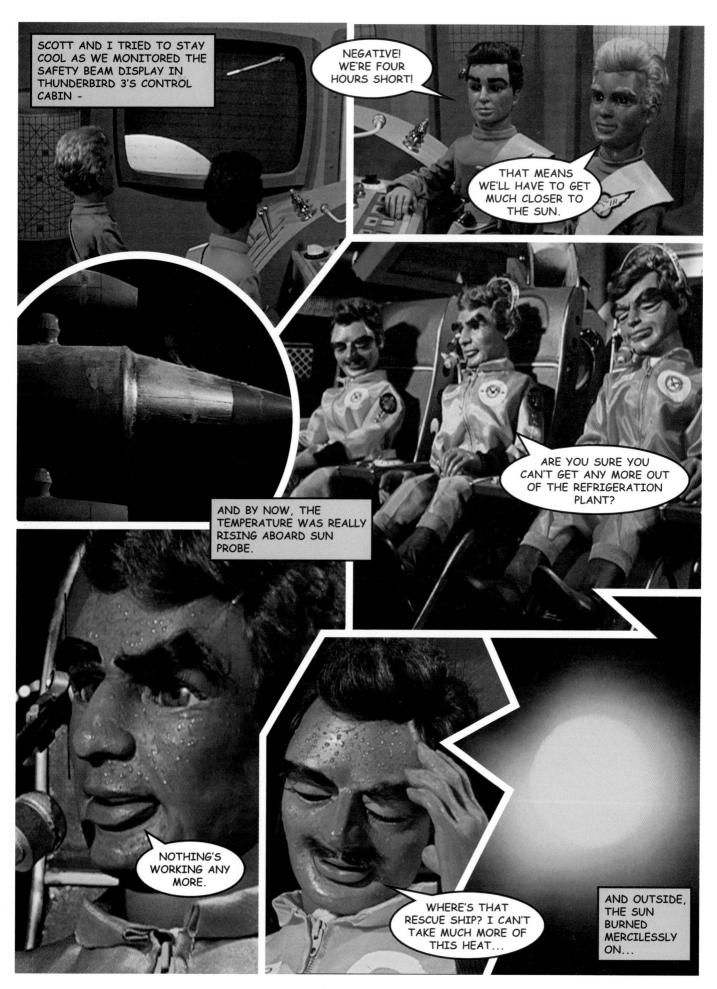

SCOTT AND I TRIED TO STAY COOL AS WE MONITORED THE SAFETY BEAM DISPLAY IN THUNDERBIRD 3'S CONTROL CABIN –

NEGATIVE! WE'RE FOUR HOURS SHORT!

THAT MEANS WE'LL HAVE TO GET MUCH CLOSER TO THE SUN.

ARE YOU SURE YOU CAN'T GET ANY MORE OUT OF THE REFRIGERATION PLANT?

AND BY NOW, THE TEMPERATURE WAS REALLY RISING ABOARD SUN PROBE.

NOTHING'S WORKING ANY MORE.

WHERE'S THAT RESCUE SHIP? I CAN'T TAKE MUCH MORE OF THIS HEAT...

AND OUTSIDE, THE SUN BURNED MERCILESSLY ON...

26

...WHILE WE TOOK THUNDERBIRD 3 TO THE LIMITS OF ITS ENDURANCE.

TRY THE SIGNAL AGAIN, TIN-TIN.

WE DAREN'T GO ANY CLOSER. THE HULL WON'T STAND IT.

YES...TRY...THE...SIGNAL...AGAIN...

IT WAS OUR LAST CHANCE...

...BUT SUN PROBE WAS STILL OUT OF RANGE.

IT'S STILL TOO SHORT. CAN'T YOU INCREASE POWER, TIN-TIN?

I CAN OVERRUN THE SYSTEM BY ABOUT POINT FIVE...

THEN DO THAT, WILL YOU? WE JUST CAN'T GO ANY CLOSER.

SCOTT AND I ANXIOUSLY WATCHED THE SCREEN AS WE TRIED ONE LAST TIME...

28

MISSION FILE REPORT:
SECURITY HAZARD/END OF
VIDEPRINT THREE

29

Name: Brains

Born: 14 November 2040

Alias: Hiram K. Hackenbacker

Special Duties: Scientist

Orphaned at the age of twelve, Brains's phenomenal scientific genius was recognized by a professor at the University of Cambridge, who provided the boy with a good home and a stimulating environment in which to develop his mental powers. Jeff Tracy's search for a talented designer to help him create the craft he needed to equip International Rescue led him to Brains. The young scientist was nervously delivering a lecture in Paris when Jeff first met him. Brains immediately recognized the worth of Jeff's project and accepted his challenge without hesitation. A dedicated perfectionist, Brains is constantly working to improve International Rescue's craft and facilities, but he still finds time for his own projects, among them his robot Braman. He also works with the commercial aviation industry as a design consultant.

Name: Kyrano

Born: Date Unknown

Special Duties: Household Management

Tin-Tin's quiet and unassuming father, Kyrano, dedicated his life to running the Tracy household following the tragic death of his employer's wife. Kyrano first met Jeff Tracy at Cape Kennedy while developing synthetic foods for space travellers. He was invited to join the Tracys after moving to France to work as head chef at the Paris Hilton. He now loves nothing more than demonstrating his culinary skills with the Tracys' atomic cooker, but his health is a source of concern to the family due to the mysterious trance-like attacks he suffers. One theory is that these may be connected to a shadowy half-brother who claimed Kyrano's rightful inheritance – their father's Malaysian rubber plantation.

Name: Tin-Tin

Born: 20 June 2043

Special Duties: Scientific Assistant

Tin-Tin has degrees in engineering, advanced technical theory and higher mathematics. Her university studies were funded by Jeff Tracy because he was so grateful to her father, Kyrano, for all the help he had given the Tracy family. Tin-Tin's qualifications make her ideally qualified to assist Brains in his scientific activities. Her adventurous spirit, love of excitement and great charm endear her to the Tracys – Alan in particular, whom she adores. She likes nothing more than to be involved in a rescue mission, despite Jeff's reluctance to put her life at risk.

Agent Challenge: Brains's Brainbuster

Challenge set by: Brains

Oh...er...Hi there...Mr Tracy's asked me to set you a dataquiz to test your knowledge of International Rescue and your skills as an agent, so I...er... Programmed Braman to come up with a few questions. Here's what he...ah...computed –

1 A malfunction in the pod loading computer system has left an incomplete record of the vehicles they hold. From the information print-outs below, can you tell which pod Thunderbird 2 should take on a rescue requiring the Mole?

1. Thunderbird 4 is the only vehicle in Pod 4.
2. Firefly is in an odd-numbered pod.
3. None of the pods is empty.
4. The Domo is in Pod 1 or 6.
5. The Elevator Cars are in a pod next to Thunderbird 4.
6. The Domo is in a pod next to the Elevator Cars.
7. The Transmitter Truck is in an even-numbered Pod.
8. The Mole is not in Pod 1.

....

....

2 These components have arrived for the spares store, but which vehicles do they fit?

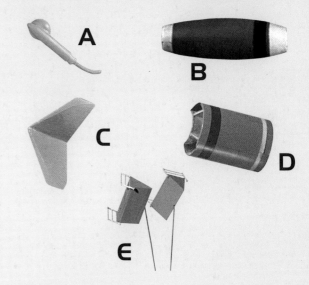

4 A submarine is trapped on the sea-bed 5,000 miles from Tracy Island. Its crew has called International Rescue, but they have enough air to last only 160 minutes. How much time will Gordon have to rescue the trapped men once Thunderbird 2, travelling at 2,000 m.p.h., has brought Thunderbird 4 to the danger zone?

3 When I'm on a special assignment, I use the cover name Hiram K. Hackenbacker. Other members of International Rescue sometimes scramble their names. Which of the team use the following cover names? And who is the odd one out?

1. Carl Yatna
2. Gary Crilvit
3. Adele Pynpole
4. Doctor Rygan
5. Ed Hooth
6. Cy F. Farjet
7. R. Kaper
8. Jory Chant
9. Tyco Scartt

5 Can you identify these twenty-first-century inventions using the letters of International Rescue? What letter is left at the end?

1. S _ DEW _ _ DER
2. SE _ SC _ P _
3. FI _ _ F _ ASH
4. _ RABL _ GGE _
5. _ U _ PROB _
6. SKY _ HR _ S _

See inside back cover for Answers.

Agent Challenge: Distress Call Detectors

Challenge set by: John Tracy

Thunderbird 5 is fitted with emergency call sign recognition detectors to pick up distress calls from around the world. Without them, messages transmitted on the same frequency would be impossible to hear and an emergency might go undetected. Using the filter colour codes, can you tell where International Rescue's help is needed from the following transmission locations?

ROCKET TRANSPORTER PLANE – BLUE FILTER

OIL RIG – RED FILTER

MONOTRAIN STATION – GREEN FILTER

R T A O H N C I D K S E E I R T S B T S A R E

D A A S N S T S C A P A T O P I R E O T P N E

L C R A A D T L E F L L O I T R N A M G F T T

O O R U S A R E I T R N O V T M I R A C A X E

P W V P E E E L S D L S I B E N A L T S E U E

M N R E N E R E Q A L U L B E D Y S E R T X O

P P C E E K R C F M T A I Y L S O L S U P I N L

O O E N O A T N S O T E L O H A D E N A L D Y P

See inside back cover for Answers.

Agent Challenge: Operation Shutdown

Challenge set by: Scott Tracy

We've been called out to the Saharan Atomic Irrigation Plant, where an electromagnetic burn-out has destroyed the remote linkage systems between the control room and the reactors. Each of the control dials is colour-coded to match the atomic rods – but which dial operates which rod? To shut down the reactor and avoid atomic disaster, we need to match the colour sequences – and fast!

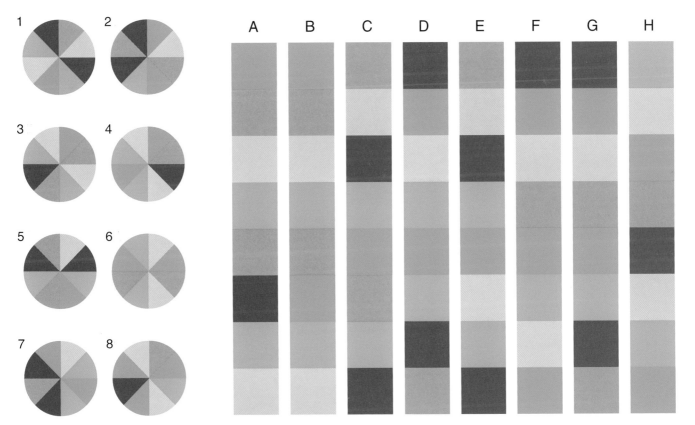

See inside back cover for Answers.

ALERT, ALL AGENTS!   ALERT, ALL AGENTS!

Alert issued by: Jeff Tracy

Top Secret...
Subject: International Rescue

Signals received by global intelligence service monitors aboard Thunderbird 5 warn that International Rescue's operations are being threatened by a desperate master criminal known as the Hood.

At incredible personal risk, one of our top agents successfully infiltrated the super-villain's hideout, but was only able to release one emergency telradio report. Weeks later he was discovered in a trance-like state wandering the Sahara Desert. His report and pictures follow.

The Hood lives up to his name. He is a master of disguise, capable of transforming his appearance with the aid of specially designed Bondaplasma masks. Cast directly from unwitting victims or sculpted from photoscans, they can fool the closest observer.

With these disguises and a criminal mastery of security technology, the Hood can gain access to the most carefully guarded buildings to carry out acts of espionage and sabotage. He offers these services to the highest bidder.

Posing as a potential employer, I was transported to his secret headquarters in the sensory-deprivation cabin of his helijet. In what appeared to be an Oriental temple deep in tropical jungle, I was shown incredible equipment and facilities. These included a complex of laboratories and a hangar full of armed vehicles. Apart from the helijet, among them I counted an All-Terrain Global Carrier, a midget submarine and an undercover Q-van.

The villainous monster also appears to boast powers of voodoo and hypnosis, which seem to be connected to a concealed statue in the main temple. I cannot believe these claims and will...

Transmission broke off at this point, and although the agent now appears to have recovered fully, he has no memory of any of these events.

All we can advise is that all agents stay vigilant. This threat to our security cannot be under-estimated.

Alert ends.

Agent Challenge: Airport Sabotage

Challenge set by: Tin-Tin

Mr Tracy's had reports from our agents' network that another sabotage attempt will be made on Fireflash, so he's sent me over to London to check security at the airport. While I was looking through the videoscan records I noticed that, apart from harmless airport maintenance activity, the saboteur had struck again. What's changed between the two videoscans? And what's the danger to Fireflash?

Report Filed by: Scott Tracy

"I'd been put in charge of Tracy Island's unexpected guest, Chip Morrison. Then Brains asked me to check out the launch system of Thunderbird 1. I couldn't let Chip out of my sight, so..."

THUNDERBIRD 1 SURE IS A GREAT MACHINE.

I FIGURED YOU'D LIKE IT.

I'LL NEVER FORGET SITTING THERE ON OUR FIRST MISSION.

I GUESS EVERYONE'S HEARD ABOUT THAT RESCUE. SOMEONE HAD SABOTAGED THE NEW ATOMIC-POWERED AIRLINER FIREFLASH SO IT COULDN'T LAND...

...AND WHEN WE HEARD THE NEWS, I HEADED OFF TO LONDON AND SET UP MY MOBILE CONTROL UNIT IN THE AIRPORT TOWER.

FIREFLASH - THIS IS INTERNATIONAL RESCUE. I WANT YOU TO STAND BY TO LAND WITH YOUR LANDING GEAR UP.

MESSAGE RECEIVED, BUT WHAT'S THE ACTION?

STAY TUNED - I'LL LET YOU KNOW.

AS VIRGIL'S THREE ELEVATOR CARS KEPT PACE BENEATH IT...

...FIREFLASH CAME INTO POSITION DIRECTLY ABOVE THEM.

WITH UTMOST CONCENTRATION, VIRGIL AND THE FIREFLASH CREW BROUGHT THEIR VEHICLES INTO EXACTLY THE RIGHT POSITION AT EXACTLY THE RIGHT MOMENT.

WITH ONE WING OVER EACH OF THE CARS...

...AND THE MASS OF FUSELAGE ABOVE VIRGIL'S MASTER CAR, THE FIREFLASH DROPPED LOWER AND LOWER.

FINALLY VIRGIL SHOUTED A COMMAND TO THE FIREFLASH PILOT.

OK, FIREFLASH – CUT ENGINES!

THE PORT WING OF THE AIRCRAFT SUDDENLY DROPPED DANGEROUSLY NEAR THE GROUND.

FIREFLASH – LIFT PORT WING. LIFT PORT WING!

THE ENGINE SPRANG TO LIFE...

...AND THE WING ROSE JUST ENOUGH FOR THE ELEVATOR CAR TO RACE INTO POSITION BENEATH IT.

CUT POWER!

OK, FIREFLASH – REVERSE THRUST.

APPLYING BRAKES DOWN HERE.

THE FIREFLASH WAS NOW TOTALLY SUPPORTED BY THE THREE ELEVATOR CARS.

BUT COULD THEY STOP THE HUGE MACHINE?

THE TYRES WERE EXPLODING...

...AND FINALLY THE MASTER ELEVATOR CAR WITH VIRGIL INSIDE IT VEERED OFF COURSE.

WITH A MIGHTY THUMP THE AIRCRAFT'S NOSE CONE DROPPED TO THE GROUND.

THERE WAS A TERRIFIC DISPLAY OF SPARKS AS IT SCRAPED DOWN THE LAST FEW YARDS OF RUNWAY...

MISSION FILE REPORT: SECURITY
HAZARD/END OF VIDEPRINT FOUR

45

Data File: London Agents

File issued by: Jeff Tracy

International Rescue's network of agents extends around the world, but none are better equipped to face danger than London agent Lady Penelope Creighton-Ward and her loyal manservant, Parker. They can always be relied upon to deal with any situation, however daunting.

Name: Lady Penelope Creighton-Ward

Born: 24 December 2039

Motto: Elegance, Charm and Deadly Danger

Born into one of England's oldest titled families, Lady Penelope inherited the determination and spirit of her father, Sir Hugh, and the stunning good looks of her mother, Amelia. Seeking a life of adventure and danger, she rejected the superficial world of high-society parties and joined the Federal Agents Bureau. Her social background provided an ideal cover for her secret work, as nobody would ever suspect that the young blonde super-model aristocrat was also an international spy. In circumstances that are still classified, Jeff Tracy discovered her talents and realized that she would make an ideal agent for International Rescue. After passing what was a seemingly impossible test, she gladly accepted the challenge.

Name: Aloysius Parker

Born: 30 May 2013

Nickname: Nosey

Lady Penelope couldn't have found a better partner in crime-fighting than Parker, when she caught him breaking into a friend's safe in a carefully laid trap. Unable to follow the family tradition and find employment as a butler, Parker had fallen in with a group of villains in the London underworld. He became an expert safe-cracker – which landed him in prison for a time. Needing help on one of her assignments, Lady Penelope decided that Parker's qualifications were exactly what she was looking for and she immediately offered him a permanent job. Realizing that the alternative was a return to Parkmoor Scrubs, Parker agreed.

Subject: Fab I

Maximum Speed: 200+ m.p.h.

Outwardly a stylish custom-built Rolls-Royce super limousine, Fab I, like its deceptively dangerous owner, is able to face any situation, however challenging. The car is equipped with an arsenal of weapons and a variety of all-terrain equipment. A radiator-mounted cannon and twin sniper-sighted

machine guns at the front, combined with rear-mounted harpoons, smoke-screen generators and dual cannons are just a few of the car's "added extras", while a Vortex-Aquajet hydrofoil can be activated for missions at sea, and in order to reach Lady Penelope's ocean-going yacht, Fab 2.

Subject: The Creighton-Ward Mansion

Location: Foxleyheath, England

The ancestral home of the Creighton-Wards since the eighteenth century, the Creighton-Ward Mansion is built on the site of earlier homes. Its elegant exterior hides a wealth of modern technology. Hidden transmitters, sophisticated alarm systems and a number of closed-circuit TV cameras are fitted throughout the house.

Even some pieces of silverware – including the teapot – double as communication devices. Many of the accessories in Lady Penelope's wardrobe conceal gadgets designed by Brains. The coachloads of tourists who are often personally conducted around the house by her Ladyship remain completely unaware of these secrets, never suspecting that they are guests in the home of International Rescue's top agent.

Agent Challenge: Trapped in the Vault

Challenge set by: Lady Penelope

Lady Penelope calling...I've just had an urgent message from Jeff Tracy. It seems that the designer of the new security system for the Federal Agents Bureau's London headquarters has accidentally locked himself into their new vault. Poison gas will fill the vault if the door isn't opened in time. Parker's knowledge of security systems is his only hope. We need to get there as soon as possible, but the headquarters are right in the middle of London. Can you help us program the computer in Fab 1 with the quickest route? There's no time to lose!

See inside back cover for Answers.

Agent Challenge: Codeword Search

Challenge set by: Parker

Cor blimey! 'Er Ladyship often gets coded messages and usually it's my job to decode them. This one's proving a bit tricky. I've looked at it every way I can think of, but it's no good. If you can find all the codewords listed in the grid, you should be left with enough letters to make the name of a right villain. Search me if I can work it out!

Jeff	Tracy
Five	Jet
Rig	Kyrano
Scott	Alert
Four	Brains
Dial	Thunderbirds
Virgil	Penelope
Three	Rescue
Test	Parker
Alan	Secret Agent
Two	Robot
Target	Firefly
Gordon	Mole
One	Island
Radio	Fab One
John	Mansion
Zero	Red Arrow
Area	Braman

S	C	O	T	T	A	R	G	E	T	H	P
S	J	E	T	H	R	E	E	J	B	A	E
R	E	S	C	U	E	F	O	U	R	I	N
A	F	C	T	N	A	H	A	K	A	S	E
D	F	W	R	D	N	F	E	L	M	L	L
I	O	F	O	E	I	R	I	O	A	A	O
O	Y	C	A	R	T	G	R	H	N	N	P
N	O	Z	E	B	R	A	I	N	S	D	E
A	D	F	E	I	O	A	G	M	I	I	F
R	L	T	V	R	B	N	D	E	O	A	I
Y	G	O	R	D	O	N	E	E	N	L	V
K	E	T	E	S	T	A	L	E	R	T	E

See inside back cover for Answers.

Report Filed by: Gordon Tracy

"Young Chip Morrison's curiosity had already got the better of my brothers, so when he asked to see Thunderbird 4 I'd have seemed pretty mean not to agree..."

THUNDERBIRD 2 POD 4

THUNDERBIRD 4'S NOTHING LIKE AS BIG AS THE OTHERS.

MAYBE IT ISN'T, BUT IT DOES A PRETTY IMPORTANT JOB.

YEAH, BUT I SUPPOSE UNDERWATER RESCUES DON'T HAPPEN THAT OFTEN - EXCEPT WHEN SOMEONE'S TRAPPED IN A SUBMARINE.

I'M INVOLVED IN ALL TYPES OF RESCUES, CHIP - UNFORTUNATELY I CAN'T TELL YOU ABOUT THEM. BUT I CAN TELL YOU THAT THUNDERBIRD 4 DOESN'T JUST RESCUE SUBMARINES.

WHO'D HAVE THOUGHT THAT AN UNDERWATER CRAFT WOULD BE USED TO SAVE A MARTIAN PROBE ROCKET?

HEY, I REMEMBER, LIKE THAT TIME AT ALLINGTON BRIDGE...

YOU REMEMBER THAT? YEAH, I GUESS IT DID MAKE THE NEWS.

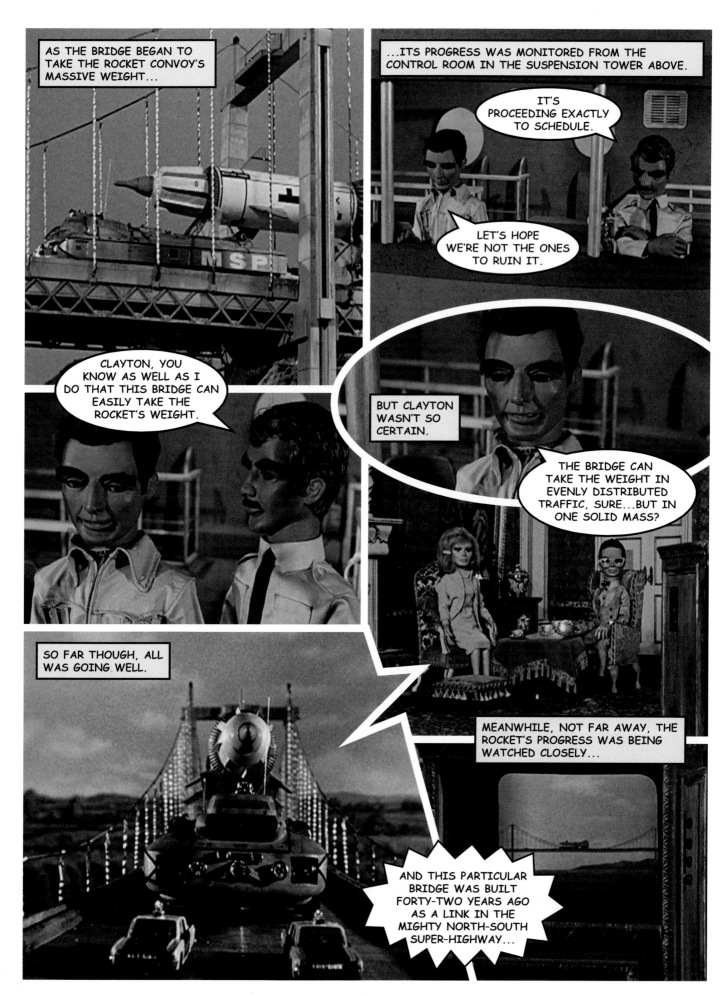

AS THE BRIDGE BEGAN TO TAKE THE ROCKET CONVOY'S MASSIVE WEIGHT...

...ITS PROGRESS WAS MONITORED FROM THE CONTROL ROOM IN THE SUSPENSION TOWER ABOVE.

IT'S PROCEEDING EXACTLY TO SCHEDULE.

LET'S HOPE WE'RE NOT THE ONES TO RUIN IT.

CLAYTON, YOU KNOW AS WELL AS I DO THAT THIS BRIDGE CAN EASILY TAKE THE ROCKET'S WEIGHT.

BUT CLAYTON WASN'T SO CERTAIN.

THE BRIDGE CAN TAKE THE WEIGHT IN EVENLY DISTRIBUTED TRAFFIC, SURE...BUT IN ONE SOLID MASS?

SO FAR THOUGH, ALL WAS GOING WELL.

MEANWHILE, NOT FAR AWAY, THE ROCKET'S PROGRESS WAS BEING WATCHED CLOSELY...

AND THIS PARTICULAR BRIDGE WAS BUILT FORTY-TWO YEARS AGO AS A LINK IN THE MIGHTY NORTH-SOUTH SUPER-HIGHWAY...

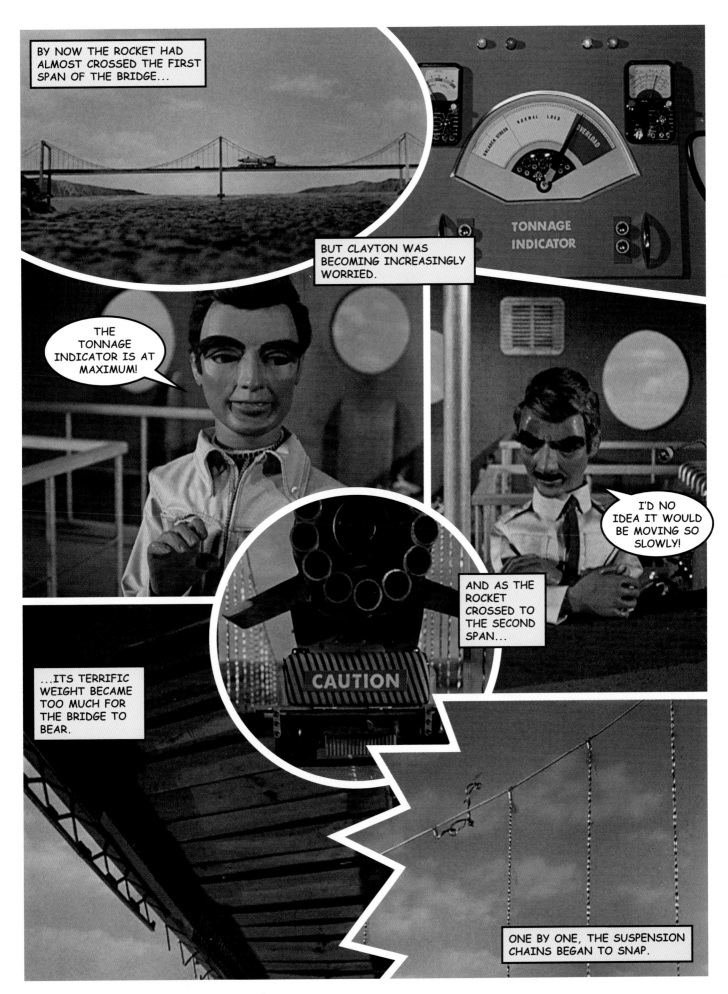

BY NOW THE ROCKET HAD ALMOST CROSSED THE FIRST SPAN OF THE BRIDGE...

TONNAGE INDICATOR

BUT CLAYTON WAS BECOMING INCREASINGLY WORRIED.

THE TONNAGE INDICATOR IS AT MAXIMUM!

I'D NO IDEA IT WOULD BE MOVING SO SLOWLY!

AND AS THE ROCKET CROSSED TO THE SECOND SPAN...

CAUTION

...ITS TERRIFIC WEIGHT BECAME TOO MUCH FOR THE BRIDGE TO BEAR.

ONE BY ONE, THE SUSPENSION CHAINS BEGAN TO SNAP.

WITHIN MINUTES BRAINS WAS ON HIS WAY TO THE DISASTER.

WHAT'S YOUR PLAN WHEN WE GET THERE, BRAINS?

I'M NOT SURE. IT'LL DEPEND HOW BAD IT IS.

AND WHEN AT LAST THUNDERBIRDS ARRIVED, SCOTT TOOK UP POSITION BY THE BRIDGE, TAKING ADVICE FROM BRAINS IN THE CONTROL ROOM.

RELEASING POD NOW!

WE ALL KNEW THERE WAS ONLY ONE HOPE FOR THE TRAPPED MEN, SO AS SOON AS THUNDERBIRD 2 REACHED THE RESCUE ZONE...

...WE LAUNCHED THUNDERBIRD 4...

...AND I DIVED INTO THE RIVER DEPTHS.